WHAT A ST...

Contents

Alison Hawes

Story illustrated by
Frances Castle

Heinemann

In this story

 Max

 Tom

 Miss Bell

 The man at the pool

Tricky words

- swimming
- stink bomb
- pocket
- laughed
- those
- clothes

Introduce these tricky words and help the reader when they come across them later!

Story starter

Max likes to play jokes on people. Each week he spends his pocket money at the joke shop. One day Max and his class had been swimming. Max wanted to play a joke. He had a stink bomb in his pocket.

Max
and the
Stink Bomb

Max and Tom had been swimming.
Now they had to get on the bus
to go back to school.

Max had a stink bomb in his pocket.

"Look!" he said to Tom.
"I am going to let this stink bomb off on the bus. It will be the best joke *ever!*"

Max and Tom ran to the bus. But Max fell. The stink bomb went off in his pocket.

"You stink!" laughed Tom.

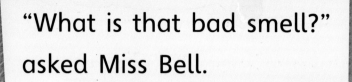

"What is that bad smell?" asked Miss Bell.

"It's Max!" laughed Tom. "A stink bomb went off in his pocket."

Miss Bell said to Max, "You can't go back to school in those clothes. Those clothes smell."

Miss Bell took Max back to the swimming pool.

What do you think will happen to Max now?

"What is that bad smell?"
asked the man at the desk.

"It's Max," said Miss Bell.
"Can you lend him some clothes?"

The man looked in a box.
He took out some clothes.

"This is the best I can do,"
said the man.

Max had to go and put on the clothes.

Miss Bell put Max's school clothes in the boot of the bus.

Max got back on the bus.
Tom looked at Max's clothes.
Tom laughed at Max all the
way back to school!

Quiz

Text Detective

- Why was Max embarrassed at the end of the story?
- Do you think Max deserved what happened to him?

Word Detective

- **Phonic Focus:** Final consonant clusters
  Page 8: Sound out the four phonemes in 'lend'.
  Can you blend the two sounds at the end?
- Page 8: Can you find four different types of punctuation?
- Page 12: Think of three words to rhyme with 'all'.

Super Speller

Read these words:

going   looked   been

Now try to spell them!

HA! HA! HA!

Q What is the smelliest sport?

 Ping pong!

Before Reading

Find out about

- What causes bad smells like body odour!

Tricky words

- tiny
- bacteria
- warns
- fridge
- breath
- sweat
- smelliest
- rotting

Introduce these tricky words and help the reader when they come across them later!

Text starter

When food goes off it smells bad. Tiny bacteria make it smell bad. The bad smell warns you not to eat it. To stop food going bad, you should put it in the fridge.

Bad Smells

This food smells bad.
But what makes it smell bad?

Lots of tiny bacteria make it smell bad.

Bad food

Bad food smells bad!
The bad smell warns you not
to eat it.

Bacteria feed on the food and
make it rot.

Bacteria are so tiny that millions could fit on the head of a pin!

If you eat bad food you eat the bad bacteria too.
This will make you ill!

To stop food going bad, put it in the fridge.

Bad breath

Bacteria feed on the tiny bits
of food left on your teeth.
This can make your breath
smell bad.

Some foods like garlic can
make your breath smell.

The best way to stop bad breath is to:

- clean your teeth
- drink lots of water every day!

Bad body smells

Your body can smell bad when you sweat a lot.

Your sweat does not smell. But the bacteria that feed on your sweat make it smell bad!

The best way to stop bad body smells is to wash your body every day.

Skunks

Some animals can smell bad.
A skunk can give off a bad smell.
The smell warns you to stay away!

Lots of things smell bad.
But this is one of the smelliest
things *ever!*

It smells like
rotting meat.
It stinks!

**corpse
flower**

The corpse flower
grows even taller
than a person!

Quiz

Text Detective

- What does the corpse flower smell like?
- Have you ever seen rotten food? What did it smell like?

Word Detective

- Phonic Focus: Final consonant clusters
  Page 19: Sound out the five phonemes in 'drink'.
  Can you blend the two sounds at the end?
- Page 17: Find a word that means the same as 'sick'.
- Page 23: Count the syllables in the word 'smelliest'.

Super Speller

Read these words:

feed   smell   make

Now try to spell them!

HA! HA! HA!

Q How do you stop a skunk smelling?

A Put a peg on its nose!